vizkids

Sayuri Tatsuya

Happy Happy Clover 5

Happy Happy Clover

FOREST FRIENDS

CLOVER (BUNNY)
ATHLETIC AND
OPTIMISTIC.

MALLOW (BUNNY)
CLOVER'S BEST FRIEND.
SHY AND KIND.

KALE (BUNNY)
CLOVER'S FRIEND.
ALWAYS THERE FOR
HIS FRIENDS AND
FAMILY.

SHALLOT (BUNNY)
CLOVER'S FRIEND.
A BOOK-LOVING
PHILOSOPHER.

TOP · FLAP · TAP · FLIP · TIP · FLOP (LITTLE BUNNIES)
KALE'S PESKY LITTLE BROTHERS.

RAMBLER THE RAMBLING RABBIT (BUNNY)
A TRAVELER AND ADVENTURER.

HICKORY (FLYING SQUIRREL)
CLOVER'S BABYSITTER.
KIND AND GENTLE.

Clover here! I'm a bunny who lives in Crescent Forest!! I love my life in the forest surrounded by the bounty of nature and lots of friends. You can find me playing my heart out with my friends Mallow, Kale, and Shallot.

PROF. HOOT (OWL)
CLOVER AND HER FRIENDS' SCHOOLTEACHER

Happy Happy Clover

WHO'S THE HONEY BANDIT?!

Spring is in full swing in Crescent Forest.

IT'S SO NICE OUT!

WHAAAT? I DID?

YOU SAID YOU'D HELP ME WITH CHORES TODAY! REMEMBER? YOU PROMISED LAST NIGHT! Just before you nodded off!

DRAG DRAG

AND JUST WHERE DO YOU THINK YOU'RE GOING, CLOVER?!

KNOCK ★ KNOCK

SIGH... I'M SORRY, MOM.

Y... YEAH...

ZING ZING

SO I MADE BERRY PIE FOR DINNER. Your *favorite.*

YOU WERE A BIG HELP TODAY.

You can drop your pack there.

THANKS FOR ALL YOUR HARD WORK.

CLOVER!

GRIN

GRIN

HUH?

JOLT

YOUR MOTHER SAID YOU WERE AT MOON VIEW FIELD UNTIL AROUND MIDDAY, RIGHT, HOOT?

WE WANTED TO ASK YOU SOMETHING, CLOVER, HOOT.

IS SOMETHING WRONG?!

SORRY TO BOTHER YOU, HOOT.

GOOD EVENING.

BY ANY CHANCE, DID YOU SEE THE BULBUL BROTHERS FLY BY, HOOT?

But...

ER... YEAH...

Yo!

Yo!

BULBUL BROTHERS

PROFESSOR HOOT! BLACKBERRY'S MOM!!

12

NOW WE KNOW WHO THE HONEY BANDITS ARE!!!

SO YOU *DID* SEE THEM, *HOOT!!!*

M-MAYBE... I SAW THEM...

UM...

I THINK I REMEMBER THAT...

OH... YEAH...

THEY MIGHT HAVE BEEN CARRYING A LARGE PACKAGE HOOT.

SOMEONE STOLE ONE OF THE POTS!!

Oh!

YOU SEE, THIS MORNING, WHILE I WAS DIVIDING HONEY FROM THE BARREL INTO POTS...

H-HONEY...

...B-BANDITS?

BLINK

SO THEY CLAIM, HOOT.

We went from flower to flower, using our wing power, yo!!!

...peach blossom nectar!! That's what we were eating!!

SHORTLY THEREAFTER, SKYE AND CLOU-D WERE SPOTTED WITH STICKY BEAKS. BUT THEY TOLD US...

WHAT'S THE MATTER, *HOOT?* YOU DID WELL, *HOOT.*

ALL BECAUSE... ...OF ME?

URK

HOW-EVER...

NOW CLOVER IS OUR WITNESS! THEIR GUILT IS INDISPUTABLE, *HOOT!!*

DOOM

Scene of the crime

Bulbul Brothers — Moon View Field

Caught Sticky Beaked

SO WE'LL TELL THEM THEY'RE *BANISHED* FROM CRESCENT FOREST, *HOOT!!*

GAK

W-WHAT'S GOING TO HAPPEN TO THE BULBUL BROTHERS...?

THEY SURE HAVE...

They've committed so much mischief already...

WELL...

OH...

NOT LISTENING

AH HA HA

WE WOULDN'T REALLY, OF COURSE.

THAT'LL SHAKE THEM UP, *HOOT.*

HOOT HOOT

HOOT

I'M SO SORRY!

I DIDN'T GO TO MOON VIEW FIELD!!! AND I DIDN'T SEE THE BULBUL BROTHERS EITHER!!!

I GOT SCOLDED OVER AND OVER.

Poor us!!

Nooo! That's not nice!!

AND, OF COURSE, THE BULBUL BROTHERS.

NEXT MORNING...

I APOLOGIZED TO MY MOM, PROFESSOR HOOT, BLACKBERRY'S MOM...

I'D LOVE TO... BUT HOW?

IF YOU GET US IN THE CLEAR!!

WE'LL FORGIVE YOU, HAVE NO FEAR!!

SEIZE HIM!

WHAAAT?

AND
...

FOR PUNISHMENT, HE HAS TO HELP BLACK-BERRY'S MOM FOR A LO-O-ONG TIME. ☆

Put your back into it!!

Groan!

THE BAN-DIT ...

...WAS A ROGUE SABLE FOX FROM ANOTHER FOREST.

TSK

GO DRY PROFESSOR HOOT'S HEALTH TEA!!

WHAT DO YOU EXPECT?! YOU CAUSED A LOT OF TROUBLE TOO!!

I thought I'd never get caught.

Clover's Mini-Guide to Crescent Forest ☆

ge **33** SEASON: The Month When Flower Honey Is Yummy

WORKS GREAT! SUPER EFFECTIVE!!
CRESCENT FOREST'S TOP THREE HERBS
CRESCENT FOREST'S MOST COMMON MEDICINAL HERBS!!

NO.3 COMPRESS HERB
PERFECT FOR CUTS AND BRUISES!

Directions
Rub leaves and place on affected area.

For
Minor cuts and scrapes, bruises, sprains, muscle pain.

You, Clover!

Guess who uses it most of all.

OUCH

So many uses...

I fell...

NO.2 TUM-TUM HERB
EASES STOMACH AILMENTS.

Directions
Pick flowers, dry, drink as an herbal tea.

For
Over-eating, food poisoning, constipation.

A hint of sweetness makes it go down smoothly. Smells good too♥

Delicious mixed with other herbs!

NO.1 RELIEF HERB
RELIEVES HEADACHES AND FEVERS!!

Directions
Dry leaves and crush. Boil and drink tea.

For
Lowering fevers. Easing headaches. Pain relief.

A little bitter?!

UGH!!

A little bitter, but works well.

OHHH...

!

CRASH

Gah!

Agh!

FLUH

OOF.

...THIS IS WHAT HAPPENED...

FORSYTHIA! ARE YOU ALL RIGHT?!!

STILL...

Okay, okay...

Bye now! Remember your promise!

ALL RIGHT, ALL RIGHT! I ALREADY SWORE I WOULDN'T!

DON'T YOU EVER, *EVER* TELL ANYONE, OKAY?!

MALLOW!!

CLOVER! YOU LOOK LIKE YOU'RE HAVING FUN.

FORSYTHIA LANDED IN SUCH A FUNNY POSITION...

HEE HEE

HEH

A... SECRET?

I CAN'T TELL!! IT'S A SECRET.

SWEAR YOU'LL KEEP THIS A SECRET!! SWEAR ON OUR FRIENDSHIP!!!

OH, WELL...

WHAT ARE YOU LAUGHING ABOUT? TELL ME, TELL ME!!

OH.

...OH.

26

STUPID CLOVER !!!

I'M SORRY!

KICK!!

FRIENDSHIPS AREN'T ALWAYS EASY...

That story you just heard... you have to keep it a secret, okay?

O-Okay. Sure...

FORSYTHIA DIDN'T SPEAK TO ME FOR A WHOLE WEEK AFTER THAT.

HMPH!

Hello!
Tatsuyama here.

BOW ooo

This is the fifth and final volume
of *Happy Happy Clover.* ☆

I hope you take your time reading
it and enjoy Crescent Forest all
the way to the end of the series! ♥

It's
Hickory!　　Oh!

TUP

DON'T WORRY! I'M SURE YOUR DAD WILL MAKE IT HOME IN TIME TO WATCH YOU RUN!

MOM...

CLOVER!! LET'S GO TO THE RACE!!

DADDY STILL WASN' HOME BY MORNING..

TMP TMP TMP

GO!

GASP

WHAT'LL I DO...?

ALL RIGHTIE... ON YOUR MARKS...! GET SET...!

I'm not losing! Me neither!

WHAT IF...

...IT'S MY FAULT?

BLAH

BLAH

WHAT IF T PAYMENT F MY PERFE TEST SCOR

...IS DADDY'S LIFE?!

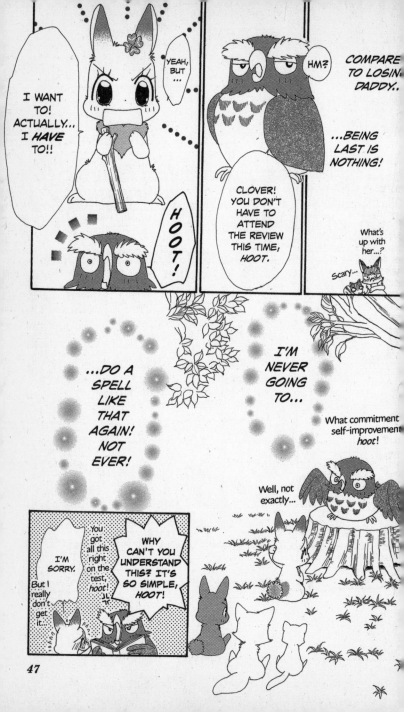

YEAH, BUT...

I WANT TO! ACTUALLY... I *HAVE* TO!!

HM?

COMPARE TO LOSIN DADDY...

...BEING LAST IS NOTHING!

HOOT!

CLOVER! YOU DON'T HAVE TO ATTEND THE REVIEW THIS TIME, HOOT.

What's up with her...?

Scary...

...DO A SPELL LIKE THAT AGAIN! NOT EVER!

I'M NEVER GOING TO...

What commitment self-improvement hoot!

Well, not exactly...

I'M SORRY.

But I really don't get it...

You got all this right on the test, hoot!

WHY CAN'T YOU UNDERSTAND THIS? IT'S SO SIMPLE, HOOT!

47

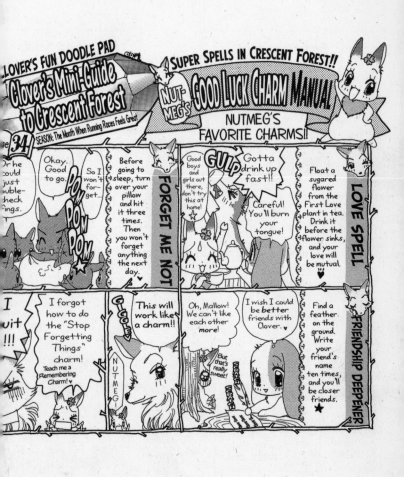

RAMBLER TAKES COVER FROM THE RAIN

RAMBLER!

I CAN'T HELP WORRYING!!!

ACHOO!

AND RAMBLER WAS COMING DOWN WITH A COLD...

RAMB-

RAMBLER!! ANSWER ME!!!

HE ISN'T HERE...

BUT THIS IS WHERE HE HUNG HIS HAMMOCK...

YOU CALLED?

RAMBLER!!

SOMETHING AWFUL MUST HAVE HAPPENED TO HIM!!

52

THE MYSTERIOUS LETTER

OH...

WEIRD! IS THIS A PRANK ...?

THREE NOW?

WE GOT ONE LIKE THAT YESTERDAY AND THE DAY BEFORE, DIDN'T WE?

A LETTER WITHOUT A "TO" OR "FROM" ADDRESS...

ANOTHER ONE!

I'LL SURVEIL THE MAILBOX!

AGAIN?!

SOMEONE DROPPED THESE OFF THREE DAYS IN A ROW... MAYBE THEY'LL BRING ANOTHER ONE TOMORROW.

THERE'S SOMETHING INSIDE... ABOUT THE SIZE OF A SUNFLOWER SEED...

CAN'T WE JUST OPEN IT UP AND FIND OUT?

No!

RATTLE RATTLE

AND NO ADDRESSES ON THAT ONE.

BUT THERE ARE *SIX* LETTERS IN HERE!

SO WE DIDN'T GET ONE TODAY.

I WATCHED THE MAILBOX ALL DAY LONG! FIVE LETTERS GOT DROPPED OFF, BUT THEY ALL HAD ADDRESSES.

Next day...

G R R R ...

Like when you were sleeping... Or went home to eat... Or...

SOMEONE MUST HAVE SLIPPED IT IN WHEN YOU WEREN'T PAYING ATTENTION, CLOVER...

TA——DA!

THAT OUGHTA DO IT!

Wow...

IMPRESSIVE. IF SOMEONE GOES TO THE MAILBOX THEY'LL MAKE A REAL RACKET.

THAT DOES IT!

N-NO WAY!

OH NO...

A ghost?! Is it a ghost?!

IS SOMETHING P-P-PARANORMAL GOING ON...?

Next day...

IT'S TIME FOR AN EXHAUSTIVE INVESTIGATION!!

We have to get to the bottom of this mystery!

WE'VE GOT NO CHOICE NOW!

ONE OF THOSE WEIRD LETTERS AGAIN!! But we didn't hear any noise!

WELL... IT ALL STARTED FOUR DAYS AGO, *SQUEAK...*

I WAS WALKING ALONG WHEN ALL OF A SUDDEN... THERE WAS A ROCKSLIDE, *SQUEAK!*

CRUMBLE
CRUMBLE

WHY SO MANY?

YES, *SQUEAK.*

THESE ARE FOR *ME?*

THERE IS AN ADDRESS, AFTER ALL.

OH.

To Shallot

From Squeak

BLUSH...♥

I WANTED TO THANK HIM, BUT...

I'M SO SMALL, HE WOULDN'T HAVE NOTICED ME.

I TRIED TO GET FREE, BUT...

EH?

SQUEAK! SQUEAK! SQUEAK!

SRTCH SRTCH SRTCH

A-ALL RIGHT!

SHALLOT! HURRY UP AND READ HER LETTERS!

BUT HE DIDN'T NOTICE MY LETTERS EITHER, *SQUEAK!*

I was afraid that might happen, so I sent a lot of them... I'm so sad, *squeak.*

SHALLOT RESCUED ME, *SQUEAK!*

ARE YOU ALL RIGHT?

I'M OKAY.

FWUP

FWAP FWAP

SNIFFLE SNIFFLE

Clover and Hickory.

      This is one of my favorite drawings of them.

    As I was drawing it, I wished I had someone
      like Hickory in my life.

CLOVER TURNS INTO HICKORY

OOH.

I WISH I WERE YOU, HICKORY...

SIGH~

HUH?

NO WAY!

BUT... *I* ENVY *YOU*, CLOVER! ☆

I wish I were you too.

YOU CAN FLY. YOU DON'T HAVE ANY WORRIES. YOU'RE SO FREE.

AND YOU DON'T GET LECTURED ABOUT CHORES...

BECAUSE *YOU* DON'T GET YELLED AT FOR FORGETTING YOUR HOMEWORK...

As punishment I'm giving you double homework hoot!!

SCOLD SCOLD

WAH

You got scolded today, huh?

HUH?

WHY NOT?

WE SHOULDN'T TALK LIKE THIS NEAR THE HAUNTED SPRING.

OOPS...

DON'T
FORGET
NOW!

HOWEVER...
BOTH OF YOU
MUST RETUR[
TO THIS VER[
SPOT BEFOR[
THE SUN SET[
...

...OR YOU
WON'T
SWITCH
BACK.

VAWN

RUB
RUB

STARE ☆

...?

I DON'T
REMEMBER
THIS TALL
GRASS...

FWUMP

DID I
FALL
ASLEEP
...?

HUH
...?

HWOOo...

OUCH...

THUNK!

UM...

WHERE AM I ...?

...

VIP

OH NO! CRESCENT FOREST IS SO FAR AWAY!!!

WELL... I BETTER GET BACK FAST!!

PLOMP

OOPS

WHOA! I HAD NO IDEA...

...A GUST OF WIND CAN BLOW HICKORY...

...ALL THE WAY OUT OF THE FOREST!

...ANY-WHERE AROUND HERE.

AND THERE AREN'T ANY TREES...

I FORGOT!! I CAN ONLY SOAR BY JUMPING OFF A TALL TREE!!!

ACK!

I'LL HAVE TO RUN THE WHOLE WAY!!

TMP

TM TM TM

TM TM

...I COULD HOP RIGHT OVER A ROCK LIKE THIS...

CLIMB

CLIMB

IF I WERE A BUNNY...

PUFF

HUFF

THE SAND IS CRUMBLING AWAY!

!

...BUT THE FOREST ISN'T ANY CLOSER!

I'VE BEE RUNNIN FOREVE

SHFF

SHFF

OH NO!! I'VE GOTTA GET BACK TO THE SPRING!

...OR YOU WON'T SWITCH BACK.

BOTH OF YOU MUST RETURN TO THIS VERY SPOT BEFORE THE SUN SETS.

THE SUN'S SETTING ALREADY!!

OOF OOF

GASP

NOW I REMEMBER!! HICKORY CAN'T FLY WHEN HE EATS TOO MUCH!!

WHEEE

WOBBLE

OH...

!

FWUMP

89

IN SEARCH OF MALLOW'S DREAM

One day, Mallo asked...

DO **ALL** OF YOU HAVE A DREAM ...?

I'M GONNA BE A CARPENTER!! You know—to carry on the family business.

MY DREAM IS, FIRST, BECOME A POP STAR, SECOND, FIND A REALLY CUTE BOY WHO—

WELL, DUH, CLOVER! THAT'S ALL YOU EVER TALK ABOUT!

YEAH!!

I WANT TO EXPAND THE BUNNY EXPRESS TO OTHER FORESTS!

Hey!! Listen to me!

I'D LIKE TO BE A BOTANIST.

I DREAM ABOUT TRAVELING WITH RAMBLER!!!

I... I'M GOING TO...

UH, FOR THE NEXT LESSON...

... TEACH YOU ABOUT ...

NGH!

GRR GRR GRR

CHATTER CHATTER

UM...

CHATTER CHATTER

JOLT

HEEEEY!

OH...

OKAY, MALLOW... ♡ GO AHEAD AND START TEACHING NOW. ♡

C'MON, YOU GUYS! PAY ATTENTION TO MALLOW!

SILENCE

THUMP THUMP THUMP!!

SHE'S MY BESTEST FRIEND!

HOW...

...CAN I HELP MALLOW?

MY GOODNESS, CLOVER!!

YOU'VE HARDLY EATEN!

YEAH... I'm not hungry.

D I N'T D A NG OR ER!

OVER! LLOW!! HEARTS N'T IN IT!! specially allow!!

YEAH!

YEAH.

YEAH.

LET'S DELIVER THESE LETTERS, THE SOONER THE BETTERS! GO TEAM!

OKAY!

For real?!

That's not true...

LOOK!! A LITTLE BUG BITE!!

!

WAAH

I THINK SOMETH... TO DO WITH HE... BACK.

IT LOOKS LIKE IT HURTS WHEN WE TOUCH HER THERE...

GOO~

I KNOW A MEDICINAL LEAF THAT WOULD RELIEVE THIS!!

WHERE? I DON'T SEE ANY-THING...

GAH

THAT WAS GREAT, MALLOW!!

SPLA...

IT DOES! THANK YOU, MALLOW!

THA... SHOUL... HELP...

GOO

I REMEMBERED SOMETHING LIKE THIS HAPPENED WHEN I WAS A BABY... My father told me about it.

NONE OF US FIGURED IT OUT! HOW DID YOU KNOW...?

I WANT TO TRY TO BECOME A DOCTOR...!!

NO... I *WILL* BECOME A DOCTOR!!

DEC

MALLOW ...

THA GREA

YOU'LL BE AN AMAZING DOCTOR!!

Today...
A future doctor was born in Crescent Forest.
☆

PROFESSOR HOOT IS CRESCENT FOREST'S SCHOOL-TEACHER → AND DOCTOR.

I'M HAPPY TOO, *HOOT*. Now I'll have help.

HOOT ♪

BUT I DON'T SEE IT IN PROF. HOOT'S BOX OF PLANT SAMPLES...

HEALING HERB

TREATS A VARIETY OF ILLNESSES AND INJURIES.
CRUSH LEAVES TO MAKE A SALVE FOR WOUNDS.
USE THE STEM TO REDUCE FEVERS.
STEEP THE ROOTS TO TREAT MANY ILLNESSES.

HOW USEFUL! THIS HERB CURES ALMOST ANYTHING!!

HEALING HERB...

WOW!!

IT ONLY GROWS AT HIGH ALTITUDES ON PEAKS SHROUDED IN FOG AND BUFFETED BY HIGH WINDS.

POINTY PEAK? THAT'S EVEN FARTHER THAN THE NEXT FOREST OVER...

That's a long way away!

THAT'S BECAUSE IT DOESN'T GROW IN CRESCENT FOREST.

I COULD TREAT SO MANY ILLNESSES AND INJURIES.

THAT'S TOO BAD. IF I HAD THIS HERB...

Hmm... AROUND HERE SOMEWHERE... ON POINTY PEAK, PROBABLY.

WHERE DOES IT GROW?

SHALLOT!!

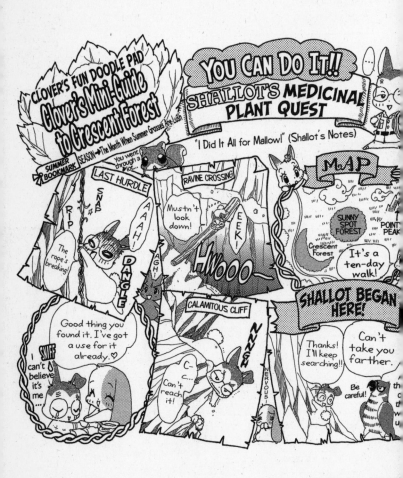

I had fun drawing this portrait
of Clover and Mallow.

It's wonderful to have
a friend for life...

..no matter how
many years go by
or how far apart
you are.

I'M... ROSE!! THISTLE'S TWIN SISTER!!!

UM... WELL, YOU SEE... I'M...

OH...

AND HOW COME YOU'RE INSIDE TH- THISTLE'S PACKAGE ?!

WHO ARE Y-YOU ...?

I JUST *HAD* TO MEET YOU!!

THISTLE'S TOLD ME SO MUCH ABOUT YOU!

THISTLE'S... TWIN SISTER?

THAT'S RIGHT!

WHAT'S GOING ON?

BIG BWUZZA!

He didn't say anything about you in his letters...

B-BUT... THISTLE NEVER MENTIONED A SISTER...

HIP HOP...

122

I NEVER KNEW A GIRL COULD BE SO *COOL!*

SHE'S DIFFERENT FROM CLOVER AND MALLOW.

ROSE IS GREAT...

ZZZZ~

WHEE!

WHAT?

ACTUALLY... I CAME HERE TO APOLOGIZE...

HEH...

WHY SO POLITE ALL OF A SUDDEN...?

WE DID PLAY PRETTY HARD...

THEY ALL CONKED OUT.

FWAP

!

...HAD A LOT OF FUN. THANK YOU VERY MUCH, KALE.

I...

CLOVER'S FUN DOODLE PAD

Clover's Mini-Guide to Crescent Forest

AUTUMN BOOKMARK

SEASON — The Month When Surprises Arrive in the Mail

IT CAME FROM SUNNY SPOT FOREST

WHAT'S THISTLE LIKE?

Sledding on grass?! Is she cute?

Books?

Does she like berry pie?

She is C-c...

Why didn't you tell me she came?!

I wanna meet Thistle too!!

FLAP★

FLAP

③

①

②

④

We're all ears!

What's she like? Tell us!♡ Tell us!♡

Yes!

She's cute all right!♥

Can't wait to meet her!

I knew it! She's cute!

Definitely cute!

YEP YEP

C-cute! Yeah!

C-c... BLUSH

SIGH

Um Um

INTRODUCING THISTLE!

Curious, energetic, cheerful.

Carefree!♥

Great with kids

Athletic!! The strongest legs Sunny Spot Forest

My favorite couple's portrait?
Why, Rambler and Clover, of course!

Every time I draw
these two, I think,
"I want them to have
a happy ending."

The bonus story at
the end of this
volume tells the tale
of their first meeting.

To everyone who has read *Happy Happy Clover*,
to those who sent in letters,
to my succession of editors,
to all who helped me with this work—
thank you from the bottom of my heart.

It's thanks to all of you that this story is full of joy.
  Thank you so much!

MIGHT
OT BE
O FAR
WAY...

I SUPPOSE THE DAY WHEN YOU'LL NEED A GOOD TENT...

MUMBLE...

...

WELL, HOPEFULLY I'LL COME UP WITH SOMETHING BEFORE I GO ON MY TRAVELS.

I'D PREFER A SINGLE PIECE OF LIGHTWEIGHT CLOTH AND A STURDY ROPE, BUT...

TO TELL THE TRUTH ...

...those are hard to come by.

NO!

DID YOU SAY SOMETHING?

PTUI!

SPICY!!

SPICY!!

LEAVE EVERYTHING TO ME!

SO YOU CAN COOK TOO NOW, CLOVER?

LOOK, I EVEN MADE DINNER! POTATO AND CORN SOUP!!

AND THEN...? YOU WERE SAYING?

OH! SORRY.

MALLOW...?

...THEN I...

WHAT WAS I...

Oh! Yes!

PST PST

VIP

SHUFFLE

VIP

...SO I PUT TOO MUCH SEASONING IN OUR FOOD; BUT ALL IN ALL THE TRIP WITH MY DAD...

...was a lot of fun, and...

WHAT IF I MISSED SOMETHING *REALLY FUN* WHILE I WAS AWAY FROM THE FOREST?!!

GASP

WHAT WAS THAT ALL ABOUT?

Very fishy...

WELL, BYE THEN!

SCAMPER

C-CLOVER!

JOLT

FORSYTH! WHAT ARE YOU TALKING ABOUT?

YEAH, THAT'S RIGHT! NOTHING TO DO WITH YOU, CLOVER.

N-NOTHING! NOT A THING!

136

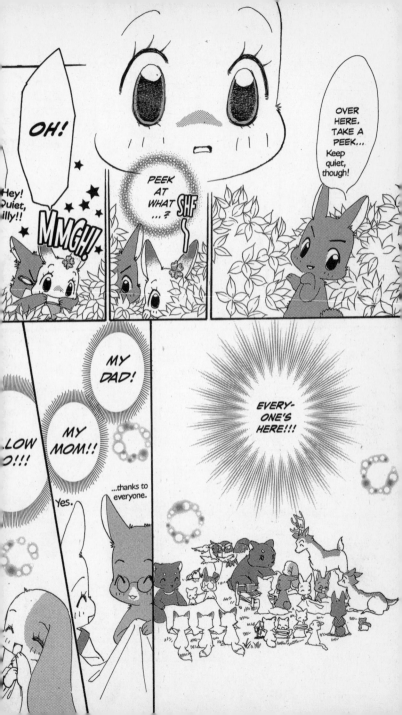

AND MAY SHE NEVER FORGET OUR FOREST NO MATTER HOW FAR SHE IS...

...TENT AND ROPE PROTECT CLOVER ON HER JOURNEY...

THAT'S WHEN YOU CAUGHT ME.

I HAD TO COME BACK A LITTLE EARLY BECAUSE MY LITTLE BROTHERS FELL ASLEEP.

SO FORGET WHAT YOU SAW, OKAY?!!

THIS IS ALL A SECRET.

GET HOME ON THE DOUBLE, CLOVER! AND HOP BACK INTO BED!

EVERYONE'S GOING HOME!

OH NO!

FWAP

ONE MORE GET-TOGETHER AND WE'LL BE FINISHED.

LET'S STOP HERE FOR TODAY. Clover's going to wake up soon.

CLOVER SETS OFF ON HER TRAVELS?! PART 1

HEY THERE.

Rambler has returned to Crescent Forest.

COME ON! TAKE ME TRAVELING WITH YOU ALREADY!!

REALLY ...?

RAM BLE !!

THERE'S NO PLACE IN THIS FOREST THAT I HAVEN'T SEEN...

I'VE STUDIED UP ON GEO-GRAPHY!!

PLUS, I'VE BEEN PRACTICING HOW TO PITCH A TENT.

I COULD HARDLY WAIT TO SEE YOU AGAIN!!

Hop

THERE'S NO NEED TO PUNISH YOURSELF, HOOT...

IT'S SO NICE BEING HERE WITH CLOVER... AND EVERYONE.

I REALLY LOOK FORWARD TO MY VISITS.

THIS FOREST HAS GOTTEN TOO... COMFORTABLE.

BUT I HAVE NO RIGHT TO BE SO HAPPY!

...BECAUSE OF ME?!!

PLEASE... KEEP THIS QUIET.

!

I'M IRRESPONSIBLE...

ALL RIGHT, HOOT.

I HAVE NO RIGHT TO RUIN CLOVER'S LIFE TOO.

MUCH APPRECIATED, HOOT.

THAT WOULD COME IN USEFUL FOR FUEL IN THE WINTER, WOULDN'T IT? I'LL GET YOU SOME TOMORROW.

RAMBLER ISN'T COMING BACK...

RUSTLE

151

I'm so glad! ♥

Look! I'm not wobbly anymore!!

AND IT TOOK ME ANOTHER THREE DAYS BEFORE I COULD WALK.

I DIDN'T WAKE UP FOR THREE DAYS.

I DON'T REMEMBER MUCH AFTER THAT...

RAMBLER HASN'T VISITED ME— NOT ONCE! WHY?!

BUT THESE LAST THREE DAYS...

EAH, BUT...

YOU TWO ARE TOGETHER NOW. SHOULDN'T YOU TRUST HIM...?

DID HE LEAVE WITHOUT TELLING ME?!!

GASP

...MAKING THE ROUNDS OF THE FOREST. HE'S TRYING TO CONVINCE EVERYONE TO LET YOU TRAVEL WITH HIM.

RAMBLER IS...

OH MY...

vas our very ond l you ke up ugh.

Happy Happy Clover—The End

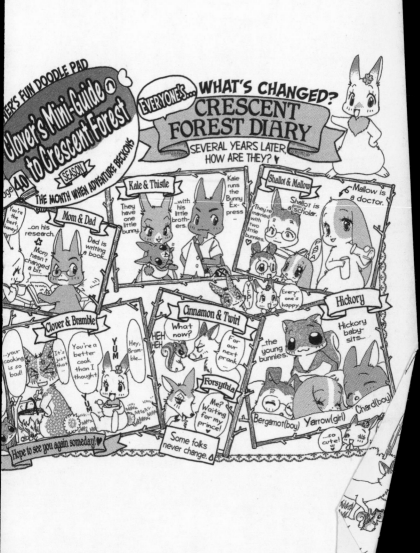

I... GET IT...

RUMOR HAS IT YOU'RE *CURSED*!

AND THAT YOUR PRESENCE CURSES THE FORESTS YOU PASS THROUGH...

YOU'RE THE ONE... THE ONE WHO SURVIVED THE FOREST THAT PERISHED IN A SINGLE DAY, AREN'T YOU?

Its sole survivor.

!

...PROBABLY ...M CURSED.

YEAH...

LIVING ON AFTER LOSING EVERYONE I EVER CARED ABOUT...

HA HA...

THE CURSE OF THE RAMBLING RABBIT...

I BET THOSE MIGRATING BIRDS SPREAD THIS STORY...

THEY'VE PROBABLY QUACKED IT ALL OVER THE AREA...

HOBBLE

HOBBLE

GASP

THEN THE WHOLE FOREST WILL KNOW I'M HERE.

WOBBLE

PROBABLY GOING TO TELL HER PARENTS ABOUT ME.

...I BETTER MOVE ON...

BEFORE THEY START TALKING ABOUT THAT CURSE AGAIN...

HOP

OH.

She hopped away...

A BUNNY!

On the out- skirts of the forest?

HEY...

A Single Drop of Water—The End

Did she fall asleep?

ZZZ...

Looks like it....

Message From Sayuri Tatsuyama

"Hapi-Clo" is finally complete. By the time I'd written ten stories, I knew how I wanted the series to end. I'm so happy now that I've drawn that final scene.

As for all the things I planned to do when I finished the series—clean out my room, read that huge stack of books, go to the hot springs... Well, I've done nothing but play with my birds. But that brings me happiness too.❤

Sayuri Tatsuyama loves furry animals! Before *Happy Happy Clover*, she created a ten-volume manga series called *Pukupuku Tennen Kairanban* starring puppies and other cute pets. In 2001, it was the 47th winner of the annual "Shogakukan Award for Children's Manga." *Happy Happy Clover* is so popular in Japan that it has been made into an anime and a Nintendo DS video game. But they haven't been translated into English yet. Tatsuyama lives in the city of Osaka in Japan. Her dream is to have a huge dog.

HAPPY HAPPY CLOVER

Volume 5

VIZ Kids Edition

Story and Art by SAYURI TATSUYAMA

© 2006 Sayuri TATSUYAMA/Shogakukan
All rights reserved.
Original Japanese edition "HAPPY HAPPY CLOVER"
published by SHOGAKUKAN Inc.

English Adaptation by Naoko Amemiya & Annette Roman

Translation/Kaori Inoue
Touch-up Art & Lettering/James Gaubatz
Design/Frances O. Liddell
Editor/Annette Roman

VP, Production/Alvin Lu
VP, Sales & Product Marketing/Gonzalo Ferreyra
VP, Creative/Linda Espinosa
Publisher/Hyoe Narita

Printed in Canada

Published by VIZ Media, LLC
P.O. Box 77010
San Francisco, CA 94107

10 9 8 7 6 5 4 3 2 1
First printing, June 2010

www.viz.com

www.vizkids.com

ke a trip with Pokémon

PIKACHU!

ANI-MANGA™

Meet Pikachu and
all-star Pokémon!
Two complete Pikachu
stories taken from the
Pokémon movies—all in
a full color manga.

Buy yours today!

.pokemon.com

vizkids

www.viz.com

amazing mind. Others don't take the time to get to know that side of Paul though. If they did they would know he is the most considerate person I've ever met. Even when he is mistreated, he considers how his actions will make others feel before he makes decisions. Granted his considerations sometimes takes us a long time to come to conclusions, but that's where I meet him and compromise and to be honest I respect his thoughtfulness. In addition to his compassion, Paul has a photographic memory making it easy for him to remember coding sequences and mathematical equations. Paul does not like to be touched so handshakes, daps and hugs are not something we generally engage in. However, him showing up to our meeting spot is proof he is happy to be here with me.

I have known Paul all my life because his mom, Auntie Danielle, and momz are sorority sisters. Auntie Danielle is the only white member I have ever met of momz sorority sisters. I love Auntie Danielle because she is down for the culture. Not like the Rachel Dolezal lady fronting[18] like she's black. She knows she is white and very proudly addresses her white counterparts who are 'a part of the problem', as she calls it, when they project their micro-aggressed racism,[19] on any black person she is around. So you see, Paul is not just my tutor we are family.

As he made his way to our normal corner and plopped down on the grey and navy bean bags I asked him where he'd gotten his shirt to show my approval of it, before we begin our deep dive into the human skeletal system. I could tell he was proud that his shirt sparked a comment from me because he smiled very proudly and seemed ready to share. Before he could respond to my question, some numb-nut[2] walks by, looks at us and laughingly asks his friend,

"When did they start letting retarded people from McLean's Psychiatric Hospital into The Plug?" He just about doubled over laughing so hard and I was immediately infuriated. I did not respond right away, as I wanted to check Paul's reaction, and determine if he had heard the asinine comment. Sure, enough Paul heard. His facial expression quickly moved from jovial and proud to hurt and confused. He needed to process if the comment was in fact directed at him and once he identified the very inappropriate comment as unacceptable, he asked me very sweetly, "This would be a good time to defend myself, right?" Even in this moment, Paul was considering others in the space. We had been discussing what defending himself looks like as well as when and how to properly speak up for himself. While I was learning academically from Paul, he was learning socially from me. The Plug was packed with tons of progressives and people who I envisioned eventually leading the tech world in Silicon Valley, with their sphere of influence and conversations I overheard them having. While I wanted to see how Paul would handle himself in this type of situation, I knew I would not allow the moment to pass without saying something profound.

I turned to Paul and said, "Why yes my brotha...this is the perfect time for you to defend yourself." Paul got up, with me paces behind, and walked very awkwardly but directly over to the ignoramus[21] who thought he was auditioning for Laugh-A-Palooza or Comic View, as my popz would say and addressed him very matter-of-factly.

Paul spoke with slight pauses in his sentences as it takes him a moment to collect all of his thoughts. Ex - excuse me sir; I'mm - mm sure, you were re - fer - ing to to me when you made that very ru – rude comment about St. Jude patients. Well, I will have you know I am not – not mentally disturbed. I have Autism Spectrum Disorder! If The Plug dis – dis - allowed anyone from com –

coming into its establishment it should be ig - norant peep - ple like you and not - not people with mental illness or peep – ple like me."

However hard it was for Paul to articulate those words I think he did a fine job of setting the record straight. The jerk however was not letting up. He went on further to insult Paul by saying, "Retarded, Autism whatever. It's all the same to me. Anyone with disabilities shouldn't be in here taking up space from people who are actually going to be making a difference in the tech world."

I could no longer hold back. This idiot was going to understand the implications[22] of his absurd[23] thoughts. I positioned myself, as I'm becoming accustomed[24] to doing, collected my thoughts and fired off.

"First of all…, I doubt anyone in the tech world would hire you or anyone who thinks like you because the tech world is made up of progressive thinkers. If your antiquated[25] thinking about people with autism is in any way related to your thought process about the advancements in technology, the tech world is doomed before it even has a chance if you plan to be at the helm[26]. Secondly, people with autism should not be deduced[27] to people with disabilities. Autism is not a disability. It's a different ability. Paul is 22 and in most cases known as a genius. He is in his first year of residency as a surgeon at a hospital that could very well find a cure to treat your level of stupidity. I will have you know he graduated high school in three years at the top of his class at the age of 16, graduated college magna cum laude[28] in 3 years as well by age 19 and finished medical school in a record breaking 3 years too. He has already found several cures to low grade ailments on top of having a photographic memory. If that was not enough, he is the most compassionate person I have ever met.

The Plug should not only continue to allow people like Paul into its establishments but it should ban[29] people like you who refuse to evolve. You had to have been taught this kind of hatred or allowed to think this kind of belittling is acceptable, but I am here to advise the days of covert oppression[3] are behind us now. If your friends won't hold you accountable as grown men then allow me to introduce myself. My name is Bobbie, I'm 13 years old and I've been raised to value people, no matter their race, color, creed[31], religion or abilities. If no one in your life has ever told you or showed you how to be kind, unfortunately, humanity has failed you but after today, you have no excuse. I would very much appreciate you showing you want to be a part of humanity by apologizing to Paul or excusing yourself from this fine establishment of progressive thinkers and find a location that will tolerate your lack of acceptance to diversity and inclusion."

At this point, I should have almost expected it but we were both utterly[32] surprised and shocked with amazement as all the patrons of The Plug were locked into the moment and erupted into loud cheers and a thunderous applause.

The young man was red with either embarrassment or fury, I could not tell which nor did I care. He did however look at his friend who he had originally laughed with and saw him clapping with the other patrons. He quickly grabbed his belongings and tried to exit the building.

He didn't get far before the owners of The Plug met him at the door presenting him with an ultimatum. "Sir, you can either apologize to Paul now or we will reserve the right to refuse service to you at any future time you wish to patronize[33] any of our locations."

This moment was sure to be the most embarrassing of his adult life. He lifted his head slightly towards Paul and was able to muster out the faintest "I apologize Paul." I'd ever heard from a grown man and he proceeded toward the exit. The crowd erupted in applause once again, this time chanting: "PA – UL, BOB – BIE, PA – UL, BOB – BIE, PA – UL, BOB – BIE...." until we reached our bean bags.

The young man's friend walked out a few moments after; I am sure very ashamed to have been associated with such a person on such a public platform for such a monumental learning experience. "Thanks Bobbie for standing up for me like that." Paul said kindly. "Paul, we are family. I would never speak to someone so rude under normal circumstances. However, I also will never allow anyone to disrespect you and I'm proud of you for standing up for yourself the way you did. Our parents' taught us to stick together. Their generation did a good job of tolerating the covert discrimination[34] they faced. Our generation is bolder, wiser and more informed to ever allow that kind of behavior to pass as acceptable. Hatred is taught one person at a time on any level and love has to be taught the same way. One experience at a time. You down for the long journey this is going to be?"

As Paul was about to answer the owners walked over to personally apologize for Paul's treatment and thanked us for advocating for one another the way we did. They offered us free recharge food that we graciously accepted and ensured they would never knowingly allow any patron to mistreat either of us at any time moving forward. We thanked them for their great customer service and Paul continued with our conversation. "As lon – long as I have autism I hav – have no ch – choice but to be down."

Paul reached out his hand to give me dap[35] with a smile on his face that was evident he felt empowered[36] enough after today to fight this battle and win.

I matched his smile in agreement, returned his dap and we finally began unveiling each of the 206 bones of the body, network of tendons, ligaments and cartilage that connect the human skeletal system for me to ace my final exam.

THE END

Glossary

1. Thought- Provoking - stimulating careful consideration or attention.
2. Yields - produce or provide
3. Ludicrous - so foolish, unreasonable, or out of place as to be amusing; ridiculous.
4. Iota - an extremely small amount.
5. Extracurricular - (of an activity at a school or college) pursued in addition to the normal course of study.
6. Thoroughly - to a complete or thorough extent
7. Intrigued - having one's interest, desire, or curiosity strongly aroused
8. Algorithms - A systematic procedure for solving a problem
9. Facetious - treating serious issues with deliberately inappropriate humor; flippant.
10. Peripheral - the outer part of the field of vision
11. Wafted - to move or go lightly on or as if on a buoyant medium
12. Ambiance - a feeling or mood associated with a particular place, atmosphere
13. Laced – To be dressed up nicely
14. Implications - to involve as a consequence
15. Autism - a developmental disorder of variable severity that is characterized by difficulty in social interaction and communication and by restricted or repetitive patterns of thought and behavior.
16. Disengaged - separate or release (someone or something) from something to which they are attached or connected.
17. Inflected - to change or vary the pitch of one's voice
18. Fronting - A facade. Appearing one way, but really acting another. Misrepresenting yourself.
19. Micro-Aggressed Racism - a term used for brief and commonplace daily verbal, behavioral, or environmental embarrassments, whether intentional or unintentional, that communicate hostile, derogatory, or negative prejudicial slights or insults toward any group.

20.   Numb-Nutt - Lacking intelligence.

21.   Ignoramus - an utterly ignorant person

22.   Implications - a likely consequence of something.

23.   Absurd - wildly unreasonable, illogical, or inappropriate.

24.   Accustomed - be used to.

25.   Antiquated - old-fashioned or outdated.

26.   Helm - a position of leadership.

27.   Deduced - arrive at (a fact or a conclusion) by reasoning; draw as a logical conclusion.

28.   Magna Cum Laude - with great distinction (with reference to college degrees and diplomas).

29.   Ban - Officially or legally, prohibit.

30.   Covert Oppression - Covert, racially biased decisions are often hidden or rationalized with an explanation that society is more willing to accept. These racial biases cause a variety of problems that work to empower the suppressors while diminishing the rights and powers of the oppressed. Covert racism often works subliminally, and often much of the discrimination is being done subconsciously

31.   Creed - a set of beliefs or aims, which guide someone's actions.

32.   Utterly - completely and without qualification; absolutely.

33.   Patronize - frequent (a store, theater, restaurant, or other establishment) as a customer.

34.   Discrimination - the unjust or prejudicial treatment of different categories of people or things, especially on the grounds of race, age, or sex.

35.   Dap – A greeting that consist of one person slightly tapping his balled up fist to the person he is greetings balled up fist as a way to say hello, usually done by two males.

36.   Empowered - make (someone) stronger and more confident, especially in controlling their life and claiming their rights.